THE BEST OF

1994

'He's been taking something for his cold'

MATTHEW PRITCHETT was voted Granada's *What the Papers Say* Cartoonist of the Year in 1992. He studied at St Martin's School of Art in London and first saw himself published in the *New Statesman* during one of its rare lapses from high seriousness. He has been *The Daily Telegraph's* front-page pocket cartoonist since 1988.

The Daily Telegraph

THE BEST OF

1994

ORION

Orion Books
A Division of the Orion Publishing Group Ltd
Orion House
5 Upper St Martin's Lane
London WC2H 9EA

First published by Orion 1994

The right of Matthew Pritchett to be identified as the
author of this work has been asserted by him in accordance
with the Copyright, Designs and Patents Act, 1988

A CIP catalogue record for this book is available
from the British Library

ISBN 1 85797 933 8

Printed and bound in Great Britain by
The Guernsey Press Co. Ltd, Guernsey, Channel Islands

THE BEST OF

*'Specialist subject:
Government crises from the
23rd to 30th of January 1994'*

Home Affairs

Head of MI5 comes out on TV

'It was the Child Support Agency that told me to eat my husband'

Home Affairs

'We've come to read your gas meters'

Gas loses its monopoly

Clouds obscure solar eclipse

Home Affairs

'I've just eaten Freddie Starr's Grand National winnings'

Freddie Starr's horse wins race

'He's the only one who can work the video machine'

What should children be allowed to watch?

Home Affairs

'He's been there since last weekend trying to put the clock back'

Clocks go back again

'You know how it is – you bite a Chinese person and half an hour later you feel like biting another'

Chris Patten's dog bites Chinaman in Hong Kong

'In London every £10 note has been through a water company's accounts at least five times'

DTI to privatise Post Office

Home Affairs

'Viewers are warned I may be upset by the next item'

'The electricians' union will be coming back, but they can't give us a definite time'

Report criticises GMTV

National Health

'Give it to me straight, doc,
how long has my bed got?'

'And when the music stops...'

National Health

Dentist refuses to treat
sweet-eating children

National Health

'This isn't Rag Week –
they need the bed at the
other hospital'

'Would you mind if some
students watch this?'

National Health

'Take me to a hospital that's higher up the league table'

'A fight broke out after they said I didn't qualify for incapacity benefit'

Schools

'We're all going to stay here until the culprit removes these school tests'

'I wanted to go to the new lesson on responsible sex but I couldn't get a baby-sitter'

Schools

Budgets and currencies

'I'd drive to Calais to buy
cheap wine but I can't
afford the petrol'

'It stands for
Gloating British'

French forced out of ERM

Budgets and currencies

'I must give up
watching budgets'

'I've come to read your
gas meter for 1995'

Outrage over cushy prisons

'There was going to be a
riot here as well,
but we overslept'

Crime

'He's on a character-building trip from Africa to stop him eating people'

Safari boy

GOVERNOR

Woman prisoner gives birth wearing handcuffs

Crime

'Typical! When you need one you can never find a member of the Neighbourhood Watch'

'Just remember kids, nobody gets away with police reform.' 'Night all'

Michael Howard backtracks on police reform

Crime

'There goes the
neighbourhood'

'Acacia Avenue ain't big
enough for the two of us'

Policeman clips youth round ear   Police to carry guns

Eastenders star in sex libel case

'Do you sell Range Rovers?'

'I always travel at 110 mph
on slip roads to avoid any
misunderstanding'

Rain hits south

'So, how long have you lived here in Sussex?'

'If you're going to the High Street stay in the shallow end'

Rain hits south

'It's to scare away the fish'

'They come back to the same
street every year to spawn'

Europe

'The Conservative Euro
canvassers are here'

'It's a Natural Law Party fly-
past for the Euro elections'

Europe

'I'm seeing a therapist
who claims he can make
people remember the name
of their Euro MP'

Europe

'Any chance of a referendum on compulsory games?'

'I'm glad we're taking a tough stand against closer links with Europe'

Europe

Europe

'Will it open before EuroDisney closes?'

'I've seen a blurred photo of a visitor at EuroDisney but I think it's a fake'

Germans buy Rover

'They've reserved all the
best positions on the
production line'

'Unfortunately it's still our
policy to buy British'

D-Day anniversary

'It's a brilliant deception –
the real D-day celebrations
will be somewhere else'

'A tapestry is no way to
commemorate the
Norman Conquest!'

D-Day anniversary

'Well, if you knows of a
better 'otel, go to it'

'We're hiding down here until
the D-Day celebrations are over'

Sport

'I blame single mothers'

'The ref sent me for an early shower'

England out of World Cup

Subbuteo gets referees

Sport

Tonya Harding v Nancy Kerrigan

Winter Olympics

Sport

Spurs under investigation for irregular payments

'We feel it wise to cancel the Fourth Test as it would be really rather near to Hitler's birthday'

England v Germany football match cancelled

Sport

England collapse against West Indies

England beat West Indies

Sport

'I want you all to
empty your pockets'

Atherton's dirt in his pocket

'Anyone for marijuana?'

Capriati in drugs shock

Politics

'Politics is all about having to take unpopular decisions'

'Oh no! You don't think our son is an MP, do you?'

Politics

'My off-the-cuff remarks over dinner have been leaked to the press'

'I used to be in politics but I couldn't stand all the swearing'

Major's 'Bastards' remarks reported

Politics

Major makes Christmas speech   Major under fire

Politics

'All I said was that most Tories were unelectable'

'Apparently, denying there is a leadership crisis is an elaborate British ritual'

Politics

'I'm not sure about his morals but he's very good at his job'

'And the next leader of the Labour Party will be . . .'

MPs' morals questioned

Camelot wins lottery franchise

Politics

'I find Labour leadership contenders these days are so dull, robotic and bland'

'Why is the Labour leadership contest being held in a country that has no interest in it whatsoever?'

Boring Wimbledon

Beef

Germans ban beef on D-Day

Ten-year-old beef on sale

Royals and commoners

'My wife doesn't understand Prince Charles'

Charles admits affair

'Prince Charles sold it to me'

Charles promotes British industry abroad

Royals and commoners

'The Prince remained
wonderfully cool and fresh with
a hint of mountain pine'

'A witness said the
gunman appeared NOT to
bow before firing'

Charles visits Australia

Royals and commoners

'It's for added protection your Royal Highness'

Charles visits Australia

'We heard that one of the three kings is bringing his new girlfriend'

Edward's new girl

Royals and commoners

'Fire, police, ambulance or the Princess of Wales?'

Diana saves man in lake

Royals and commoners

Goodbye *Britannia*

'Sir Tom, have you met
Sir Dick and Sir Harry?'

Classless honours

Defence cuts

'You'll be on your own with
only unemployment benefit
to live on'

'We may need that back'

Defence cuts

'We'd like 259 Challenger tanks and 3,000 troops please'

Defence cuts

IRA bombs go off at Heathrow

Football match played in Bosnia

Pergau Dam

'Actually, this dam is just part of a huge arms deal'

'Sometimes I think they're just trying to be controversial'

Pergau Dam

'Hopefully the British will now sell us something to blow it up with'

'I'm afraid the arms industry has become briefly entangled with financial aid'

Dogs

Man trains dog to swim Channel

'Quick, Lassie, go and sell my story to the tabloids'

Climber sells rescue story

Right to smack

'Smacking or non smacking?'

'Let's get this right-to-smack business in perspective'

Sex surveys

'Er . . . sorry, no. I'm saving myself for the right survey'

What women really want

Hard times

'It is and so am I'

'DON'T JUMP!'

Hard times

'I've come to read the
Appointments Section of
your newspaper'

'I find all these downtrodden
home owners a bit of an eyesore'

Major attacks homeless

Hubble telescope in need of repair

Hubble telescope in need of repair

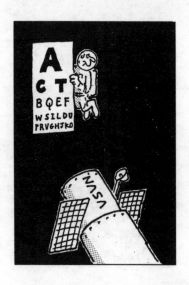

Foreign affairs

'Foreign correspondents – millions of them!'

Election

Earthquake

BBC

'How does it feel not being
able to ask people how
it feels?'

'And now, back to the studio'

Gay honeymooners

Gatt

'There remain a few obstacles to the free movement of presents over the Christmas period'

'We say tomato, you say tomado, let's call the whole thing off . . .'

Free trade talks temporarily break down

No smoking

'It's the only place you can smoke without being detected'

'We take a very dim view of smoking-related illnesses'

US Army bans smoking

Hospitals refuse to treat smokers

Religion

'Disgraceful – people should be going to the shops on Sundays'

'If I'm supplying the drink for your wedding I'd like to see you in here more often on Sundays'

Religion

'Something for the weekend, sir?'

Betting allowed on Sunday

Pope refuses to condone contraception

Religion

'. . . And please let the
supermarket have an
iceberg lettuce left'

'Let's just say we encourage
our employees to work
on Sundays'

Religion

'More tea, vicar?'

Vicars' stipends go down

Religion

Bishop of Durham ruins Christmas

Religion

'First a vicar who doesn't believe in God and now the butcher's become a vegetarian'

'When is the atheists' service?'

The vicar who didn't believe in God

Politically correct

Romeo and Juliet condemned by teacher as 'heterosexist'

Irishman awarded damages for jokes

Art

'All the truly great demolition men were criticised in their own lifetime'

Council demolishes Turner Prize winner

'I once tried to do modern art but it all got stuck to the bottom of the pan'

Neon rice field causes a stir

Trains and strikes

'You've walked too far. This ticket is only for zone one'

Tube blackout

'I'm here, I'm staying and if one comes in the autumn I'll be waiting'

Major replies to challengers

Trains and strikes

'Last year it was crop circles;
now you say you've seen a
train on a Wednesday'

'Passengers waiting for the
13.22 are advised to use
a high factor sun cream'

Trains and strikes

'This is a nice quiet spot'

'But be sure to finish your journey by 12 noon, Cinderella'

Trains and strikes

'Cheer up, it'll soon be
Wednesday'

'You'll be perfectly safe here'